Who Wants To Wear Boots?

Dec 25 2012

Who Wants To Wear Boots?

Merry Christmas
Ellie

By LORA LEE CURTISS

Lora Lee Curtiss

Singing River Publications, Inc.
Ely, Minnesota

Who Wants to Wear Boots
by Lora Lee Curtiss

Illustrations by:
Chi-Chi Walstad-Miller

Layout and Production by:
Charles Morello
IRIS Enterprises
Eveleth, MN 55734

Published by

Singing River Publications, Inc.
P.O. Box 72
Ely, MN 55731
www.singingriverpublications.com

ISBN: 0-9759953-3-2

1. Children's Stories; 2. Humor;

Dedication

To Chi-Chi Walstad-Miller the Illustrator

Look down at your feet. In the winter when it is cold
and when it is snowy, how many boots do you have to
put on? What if animals had to wear boots?

Think about a dog. How many boots would a dog have to wear? Think about a turtle. How many boots would he have to wear?

Can you think of an animal which has no feet at all? He could not wear boots even though he lives all the time in the water. He is a . . .

fish.
A fish is the wettest one there is.
At swimming and diving he's a whiz.
In the water he cannot be beat.
No boots for him cause he has NO feet.

In the ocean lives a big, big animal which has no feet.
It is a . . .

8

whale.
Of all the fishes in the sea,
Mr. Whale I'd like to be.
With no feet and a tail so flat,
He never needs BOOTS so that's that.

In the grass lives an animal which has no feet. Would
you like to be a . . .

snake?
No legs, no feet on Miss Snake.
Boots for her would be a mistake.

Did you know that some animals have more feet than you? There are many animals which would have to pull on FOUR boots. Can you think of an animal which has FOUR feet and lives in a pouch?

Little baby kangaroos
Never wear BOOTS or shoes.
If they wore them in mother's pouch,
Don't you think she'd holler, "Ouch"?

What big, big animal would have to wear four boots?

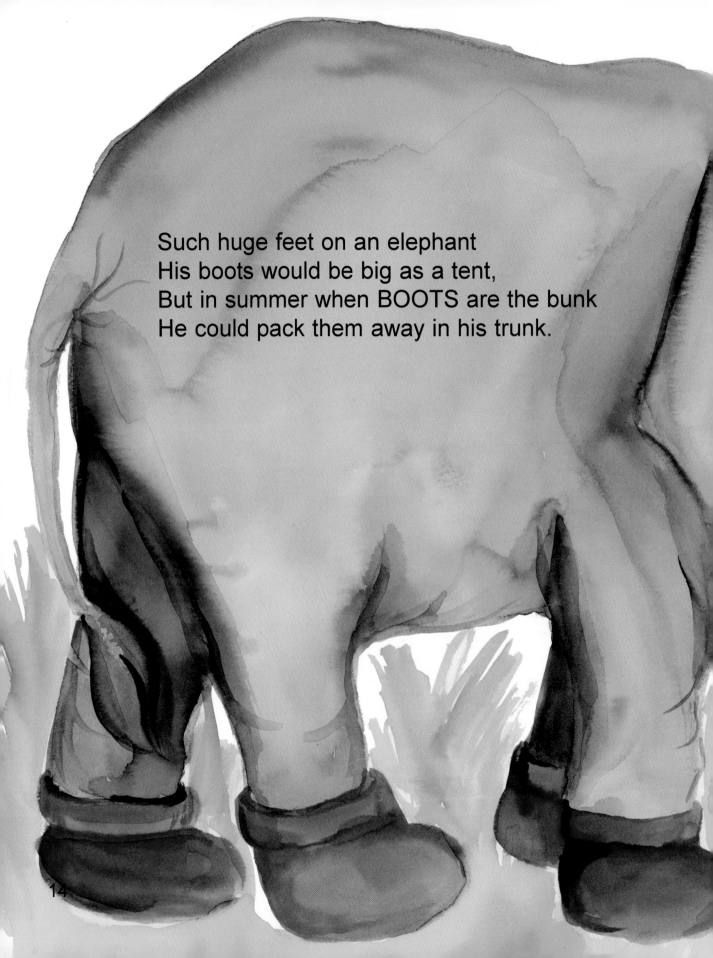

Such huge feet on an elephant
His boots would be big as a tent,
But in summer when BOOTS are the bunk
He could pack them away in his trunk.

14

In a jungle swamp lives another animal which has four feet. He is an . . .

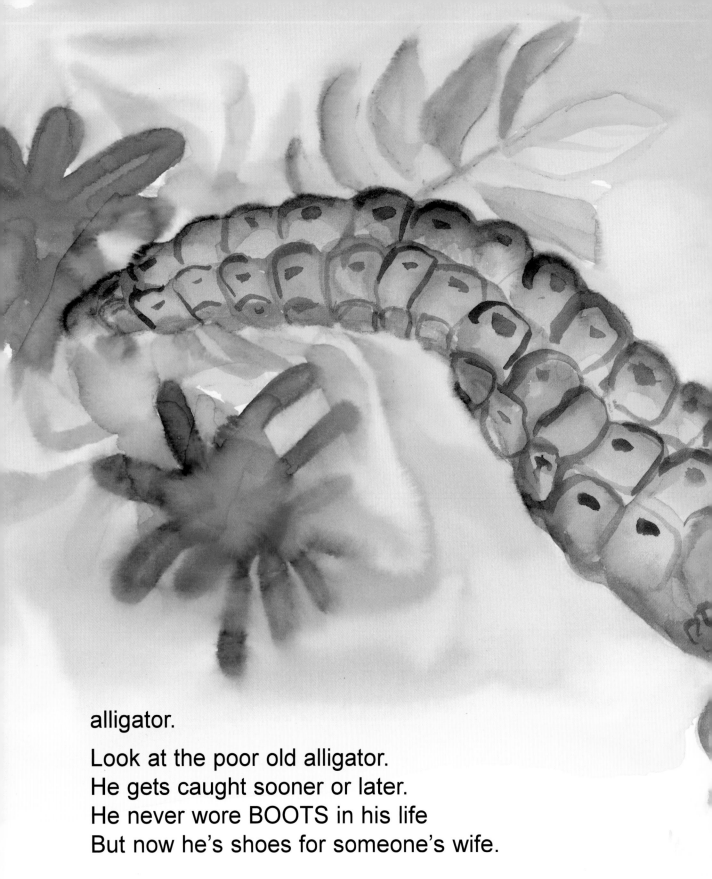

alligator.

Look at the poor old alligator.
He gets caught sooner or later.
He never wore BOOTS in his life
But now he's shoes for someone's wife.

Can you think of an animal which would LIKE to have boots to wear? He has white fur and lives in the cold north. He is a . . .

17

polar bear.

All my life I sit on ice.
BOOTS for me sure would be nice.

Another animal which would be happy to wear
BOOTS would be a . . .

horse.

Count the four shoes on Mr. Horse.
And horseshoes are lucky of course.
But when it rains and he gets wet
He'd trade his shoes for BOOTS I bet.

What small animal lives in a pond, has four feet,
and would LIKE to wear boots?

A frog.
"It's chilly here on my water lily.
If I wore BOOTS would you call me silly?"

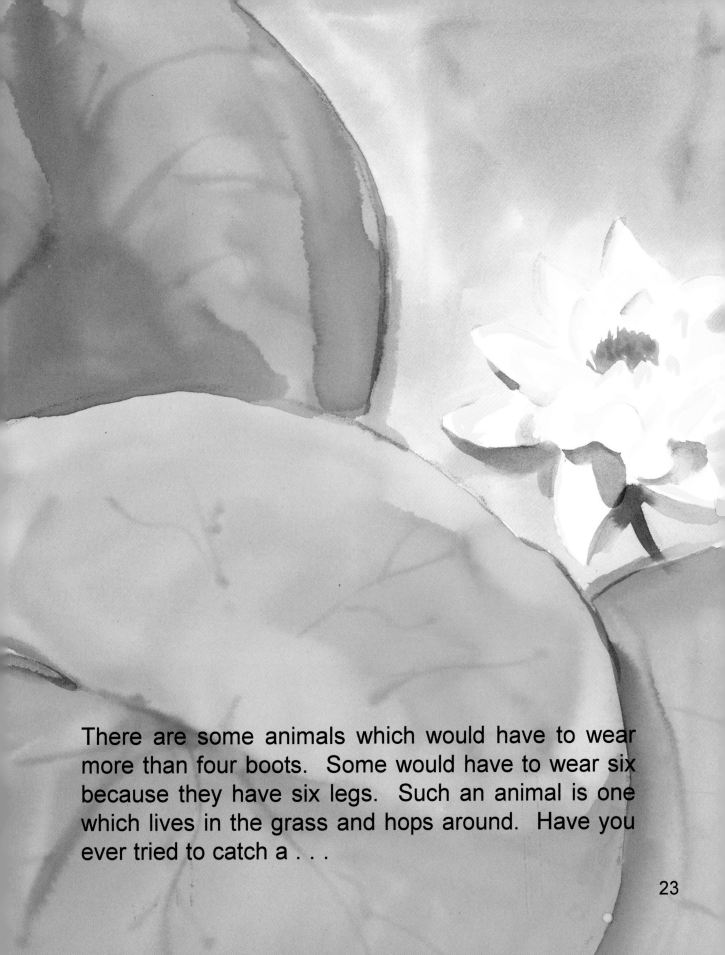

There are some animals which would have to wear more than four boots. Some would have to wear six because they have six legs. Such an animal is one which lives in the grass and hops around. Have you ever tried to catch a . . .

grasshopper.
"Would it be proper to stop her
To put BOOTS on a grasshopper?"

Did you ever count the legs on a fly or on a mosquito? These animals are called insects. All insects have six legs. This is what they would say:

"BOOTS for me?. . . Six will do.
Feet I have two

        and two

               and two."

Mosquitoes are insects too. Watch out for them, they
like to bite you.

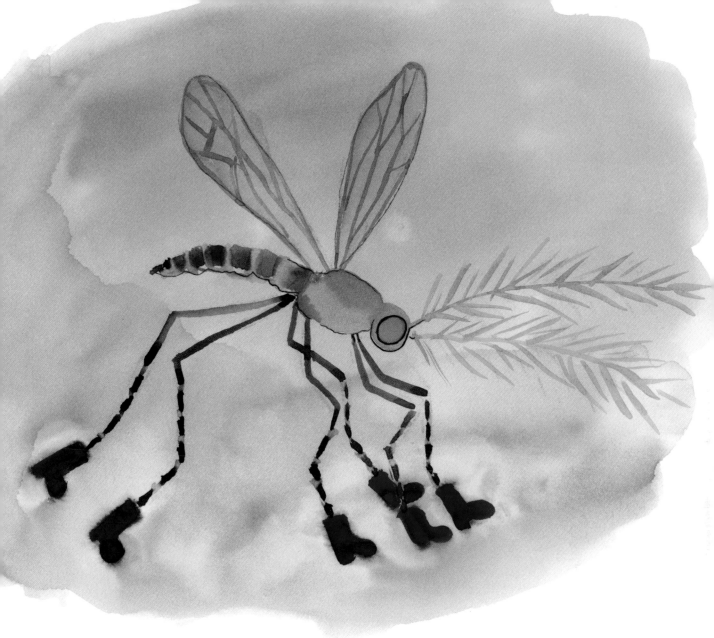

Mosquitoes fly at night.
It's you they like to bite.
But they couldn't sneak up on you so
If on all SIX feet BOOTS had to go.

There's an animal which would need EIGHT boots. It
has eight arms and lives in the ocean. Do you know
what animal that would be?

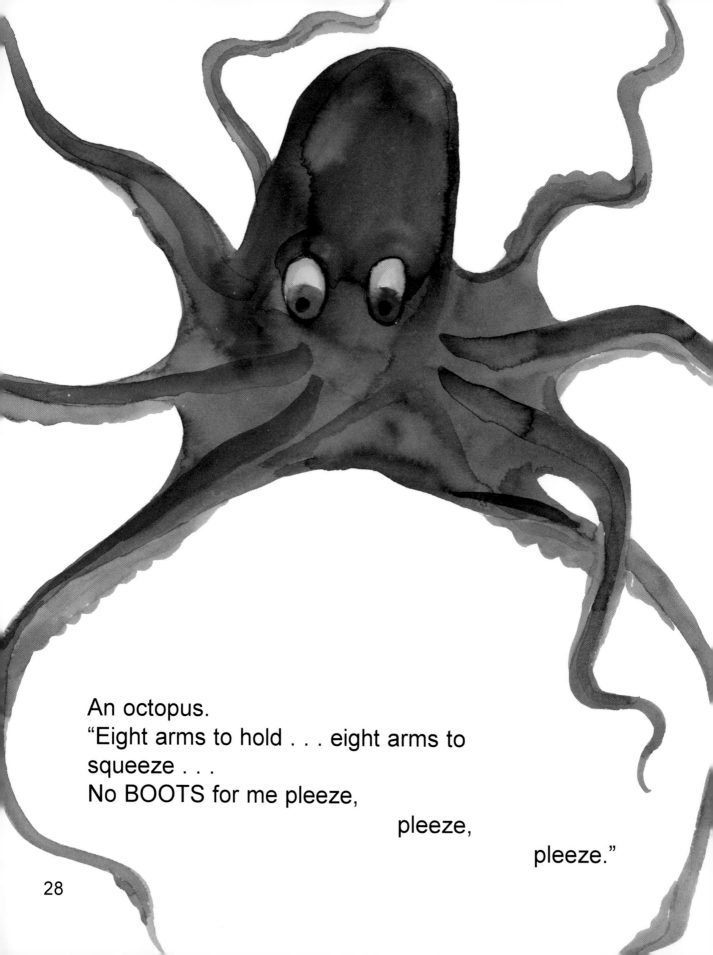

An octopus.
"Eight arms to hold . . . eight arms to
squeeze . . .
No BOOTS for me pleeze,

                  pleeze,

                          pleeze."

28

Would you like to have to put on EIGHT boots every day. That's nothing. There is a kind of worm which would have to put on a HUNDRED boots. That kind of worm is called a centipede.

"Boots for me? I'd need too many.
I'd have to have a HUNDRED if I had any."

Could you pull on a HUNDRED boots every day? There is another kind of worm. It is called a millipede. That means it has a THOUSAND legs. How long would that take to put on a thousand boots?

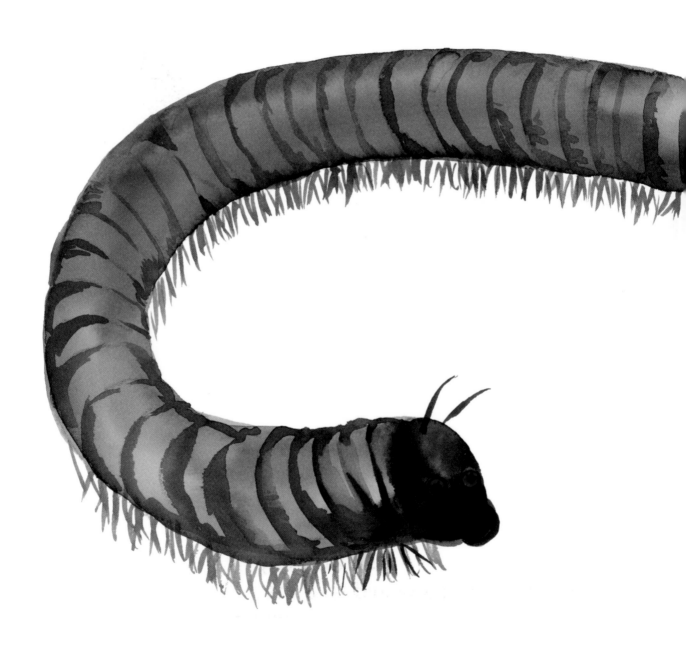

"A thousand legs are mine,"
so they say,
"To put on BOOTS would take me
all day."

Now then, aren't you glad you only have to put on two boots? Next time it's snowy, don't grumble or fuss–
just be glad you are one of us.